PRiNCESS CANDY

THE GREEN QUEEN OF MEAN

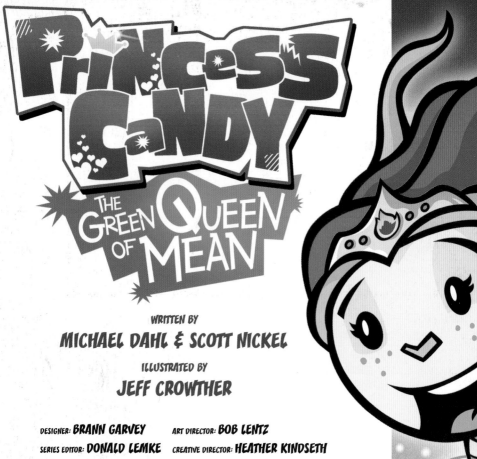

PRINCESS CANDY

THE GREEN QUEEN OF MEAN

WRITTEN BY

MICHAEL DAHL & SCOTT NICKEL

ILLUSTRATED BY

JEFF CROWTHER

DESIGNER: **BRANN GARVEY**   ART DIRECTOR: **BOB LENTZ**

SERIES EDITOR: **DONALD LEMKE**   CREATIVE DIRECTOR: **HEATHER KINDSETH**

ASSOC. EDITOR: **SEAN TULIEN**   EDITORIAL DIRECTOR: **MICHAEL DAHL**

PRODUCTION SPECIALIST: **MICHELLE BIEDSCHEID**

Raintree is an imprint of Capstone Global Library Limited, a company incorporated in England and Wales
having its registered office at 264 Banbury Road, Oxford, OX2 7DY – Registered company number: 6695582

www.raintree.co.uk
myorders@raintree.co.uk

Text © Capstone Global Library Limited 2019
The moral rights of the proprietor have been asserted

ISBN 978 1 4747 8232 6
22 21 20 19
10 9 8 7 6 5 4 3 2 1

Printed and bound in India

British Library Cataloguing in Publication Data
A full catalogue record for this book is available from the British Library.

Late one night, in Midnight City Park . . .

8

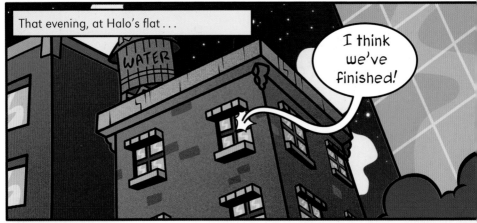

That evening, at Halo's flat . . .

I think we've finished!

This is going to be a brilliant report!

Yeah, much better than Doozie's.

I'll save the report on my memory stick and bring it to school tomorrow.

Well, I have to go. My little ones will be hungry.

You've got pets?

Meanwhile, back in Halo's room . . .

SWIPE

I can't wait for your report tomorrow, Halo.

I'm sure it'll be **electrifying!** Ha ha ha!

The next morning . . .

. . . and that's how we can save the planet.

Any questions?

Only one, Miss Hiss. Is it hard being so perfect?

And now, last, and I'm sure least, Halo and Flora.

Almost ready, Mr. Slink. I'm just plugging the stick into the computer.

CLICK!

After school . . .

I can't believe Mr. Slink gave us a detention!

And the explosion wasn't even our fault!

Tough luck about that virus, Halo.

But I knew you'd find a way to fail.

Oopsy!

ZAP!

Doozie, that's littering!

The caretaker will pick it up. It is his job, after all.

23

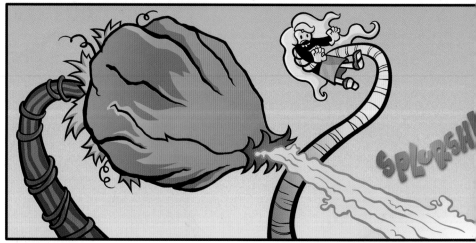

28

SUPER-VILLAIN

Villain facts

First appearance
Princess Candy: Green Queen of Mean

Real name............................Flora Fawn

Occupation..................Student, activist

Height....................................1.5 metres

Weight...............................35 kilograms

Eyes...............................Cucumber green

Hair.................................Muddy brown

Special powers
Can conjure fighting flowers, clinging vines and snarling Snapdragons. Flora has total control over all things Green.

Most gardeners weed their gardens, but Flora Fawn has a completely different kind of weeding to do. This tree hugger is trying to clean up Mother Earth, but not everyone wants to listen to her helpful tips for saving the planet. Anyone who doesn't heed her warnings faces Flora's recycling rage, transforming her into the ferocious . . . Green Queen! With several vicious plant pets at her disposal, the Green Queen gives a new meaning to the phrase "flower power". Enemies of nature beware – the Green Queen won't hesitate to turn litterers into plant food for her leafy minions.

PRINCESS PUZZLERS

Q: How long does it take a non-recycled aluminium can to decompose, or break down, on its own?

A: More than 500 years.

Q: How long does it take to recycle an old newspaper into a new one?

A: Just seven days!

Q: How much waste paper is thrown away instead of recycled every year in the UK?

A: Enough paper to fill 103,000 double decker buses!

About The Author

Michael Dahl has written more than 200 books for children and young adults. He is the creator of Princess Candy and author of *Sugar Hero* and *The Marshmallow Mermaid*, two other books in the series.

Scott Nickel works at Paws, inc., Jim Davis's famous Garfield studio. He has written dozens of children's books, including *Jimmy Sniffles vs The Mummy*, *Secret of the Summer School Zombies* and *Wind Power Whiz Kid*. Scott lives in Indiana, USA, with his wife, two sons, six cats and several sea monkeys.

About The Illustrator

Jeff Crowther has been drawing comics for as long as he can remember. Since graduating from college, Jeff has worked on a variety of illustrations for clients including Disney, *Adventures Magazine*, and *Boy's Life* magazine. He also wrote and illustrated the webcomic *Sketchbook* and has self-published several mini-comics. Jeff lives in Ohio, USA, with his wife, Elizabeth, and their children, Jonas and Noelle.

Glossary

brilliance being very clever

compost dead organic matter used to fertilize soil

environment the natural world of the land, sea and air

fatal causing death, or deadly

memory stick a small, high-tech device used to save and store computer files

organic using only natural products and no chemicals or pesticides

pollution harmful materials that damage or contaminate the air, water or soil

reduce to make something smaller or less

thoughtlessness if you are thoughtless, you do not consider the consequences of your actions

tree hugger sometimes used as an insult against people who want to protect the environment

DISCUSSION QUESTIONS

1. At the end of this book, why do you think Doozie Hiss changed her mind about recycling?

2. Recycling aluminium cans is a good way to help reduce waste. What are some other things you can do to make the world a better place?

3. Halo has to team up with Flora for a class presentation. Do you prefer to do homework alone, or would you rather do group work? Why?

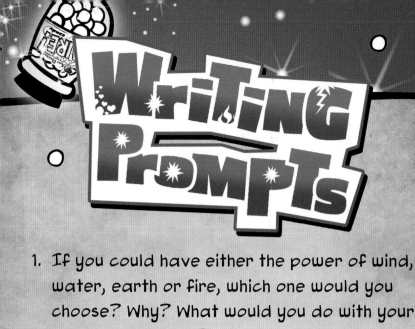

WRITING PROMPTS

1. If you could have either the power of wind, water, earth or fire, which one would you choose? Why? What would you do with your new superpowers?

2. What would have been a better way for Flora to explain how important it is to recycle? Write a letter from Flora to a friend explaining why littering is bad.

3. Imagine that one of Flora's plant creations is out of control, and only Halo can stop it. First, draw a picture of this new plant monster. Then, write a short story about how Halo overcomes her leafy foe!